Nathan Levy's
Test Booklet
of
Basic Knowledge
For Every American
Over 9 Years Old

By Nathan Levy

N.L. Associates, Inc.
PO Box 1199
Hightstown, NJ 08520-0399

ISBN 1-878347-60-8

Printed in the United States of America

List America's first colonies:

1 _____
2 _____
3 _____
4 _____
5 _____
6 _____
7 _____
8 _____
9 _____
10 _____
11 _____
12 _____
13 _____

NAME 4 WARS FOUGHT BY THE UNITED STATES:

1 _____

2 _____

3 _____

4 _____

IDENTIFY THE FOLLOWING PRESIDENTS OF THE USA:

1 THE FIRST PRESIDENT_____

2 THE PRESIDENT IN 1863_____

3 THE CURRENT PRESIDENT_____

4 THE ONLY 4-TERM PRESIDENT_____

NAME THE CONTINENTS:

1 _____

2 _____

3 _____

4 _____

5 _____

6 _____

7 _____

NAME THE OCEANS:

1 _____

2 _____

3 _____

4 _____

NAME 2 ALLIES OF THE UNITED STATES IN WARS FOUGHT IN 1914-1918 AND 1941-1945:

1 _____

2 _____

NAME 1 ENEMY OF THE UNITED
STATES DURING WARS FOUGHT
IN 1914-1918 AND 1941-1945

_____

NAME 2 NEW ENGLAND STATES:

1 _____

2 _____

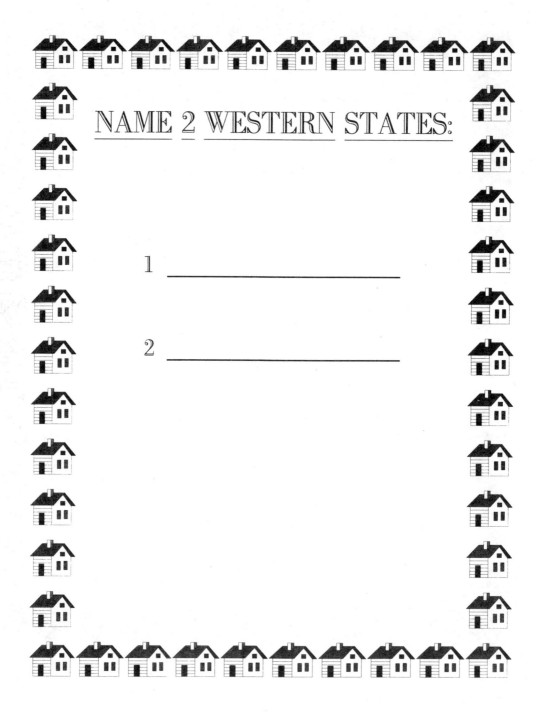

NAME 2 WESTERN STATES:

1 _____

2 _____

IN WHAT STATE IS:

LOS ANGELES? _____

DALLAS? _____

MIAMI? _____

SAN FRANCISCO? _____

NEW YORK CITY? _____

CHICAGO? _____

IN WHAT COUNTRY IS:

PARIS? _____

LONDON? _____

TOKYO? _____

MOSCOW? _____

BROOKLYN? _____

NAME THE KNOWN PLANETS

1 _____

2 _____

3 _____

4 _____

5 _____

6 _____

7 _____

8 _____

9 _____

NAME 2 DOCUMENTS
IMPORTANT TO AMERICANS:

1 _____

2 _____

NAME 2 FAMOUS CLASSICAL COMPOSERS:

1 _____

2 _____

NAME 2 FAMOUS ARTISTS:

1 _____

2 _____

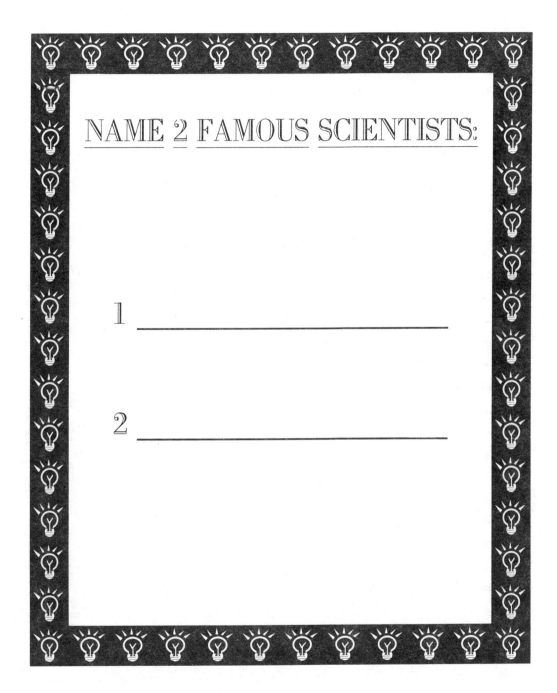

NAME 2 FAMOUS SCIENTISTS:

1 _____

2 _____

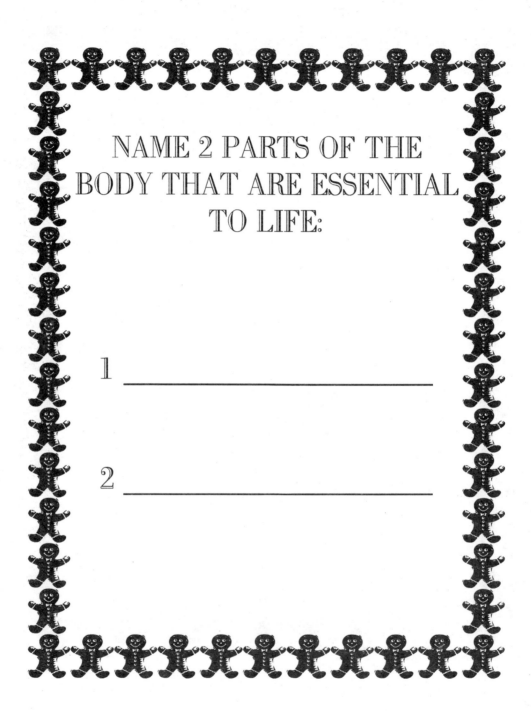

NAME 2 PARTS OF THE
BODY THAT ARE ESSENTIAL
TO LIFE:

1 _____

2 _____

MATCH THE PERSON WITH THE EVENT OR DESCRIPTION:

_____ADOLF HITLER

_____CHRISTOPHER COLUMBUS

_____THOMAS JEFFERSON

_____PATRICK HENRY

_____JACKIE ROBINSON

_____SANDRA DAY O'CONNOR

_____MARTIN LUTHER KING

A) CIVIL RIGHTS LEADER
B) BROKE COLOR BARRIER IN MAJOR LEAGUE BASEBALL
C) FIRST FEMALE SUPREME COURT JUSTICE
D) VILLAIN DURING THE WAR BETWEEN THE U.S. AND GERMANY
E) CREDITED WITH DISCOVERING AMERICA
F) "GIVE ME LIBERTY OR GIVE ME DEATH"
G) WROTE "THE DECLARATION OF INDEPENDENCE"

NAME THE COLORS OF THE RAINBOW:

1 _____

2 _____

3 _____

4 _____

5 _____

6 _____

7 _____

NAME 2 BOOK SOURCES FOR ACQUIRING INFORMATION:

1 _____

2 _____

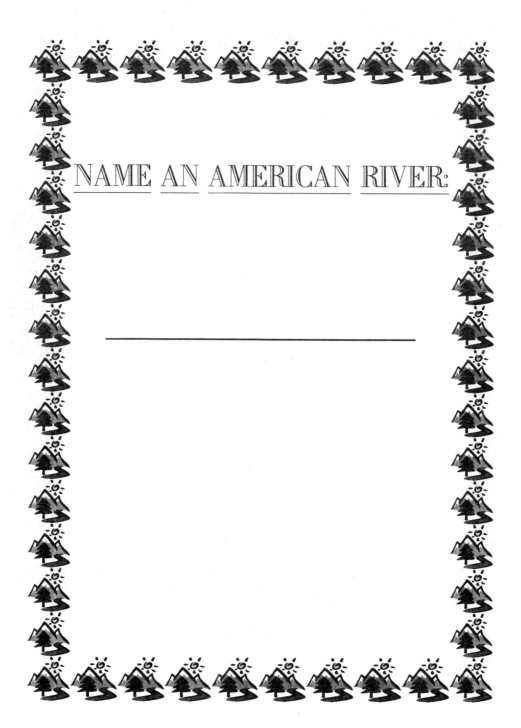

NAME AN AMERICAN RIVER:

_____

NAME 1 PLAY BY SHAKESPEARE:

_____

WRITE THESE FRACTIONS AS DECIMALS:

1   1/2   _____

2   2/8   _____

3   5/5   _____

4   3/10   _____

A STORY ABOUT SOMEONE'S
LIFE IS:

EITHER

A _____

OR

AN _____

THE 3 STATES OF WATER ARE:

1 _____

2 _____

3 _____

ANSWER KEY
(Some questions may have additional answers)

1. America's First Colonies:
- Connecticut
- Delaware,
- Georgia
- Maryland
- Massachusetts
- New Hampshire
- New Jersey
- New York
- North Carolina
- Pennsylvania
- Rhode Island
- South Carolina
- Virginia

2. 4 Wars Fought By the United States:
- Revolutionary War
- Civil War
- War of 1812
- World War I
- World War II
- Korean War
- VietNam
- Persian Gulf War
-

3. Presidents:
- The First President: George Washington
- The President in 1863: Abraham Lincoln
- The Current President: _____
- The Only 4-Term President: Franklin Delano Roosevelt

4. The 7 Continents:
- Africa
- Antarctica
- Asia
- Australia
- Europe
- North America
- South America

5. The 4 Oceans:
- Arctic Ocean
- Atlantic Ocean
- Indian Ocean
- Pacific Ocean

6. 2 Allies of the U.S. in 1914-1918 & 1941-45:
- Britain
- France

7. 1 Enemy of the U.S. in 1914-1918 & 1941-1945:
- Germany

8. New England States:
- Connecticut
- Massachusetts
- Rhode Island
- New Hampshire
- Maine
- Vermont

9. Western States:
- Washington
- Oregon
- California
- Idaho
- Nevada
- New Mexico
- Utah
- Montana

10. Cities in States:
- Los Angeles is in California
- Dallas is in Texas
- Miami is in Florida
- San Francisco is in California
- New York City is in New York
- Chicago is in Illinois

11. Cities in Countries:
- Paris is in France
- London is in England (Britain)
- Tokyo is in Japan
- Moscow is in Russia
- Brooklyn is in the United States (America)

12. The 9 Planets:
- Mercury
- Mars
- Earth
- Jupiter
- Neptune
- Saturn
- Venus
- Uranus
- Pluto

13. Two Famous Documents For Americans:
- Declaration of Independence
- The Constitution
- Mayflower Compact
- Emancipation Proclamation

14. Famous Classical Composers:
- Bach
- Mozart
- Beethoven
- Handel
- Tchaikovsky
- Chopin

15. Famous Artists:

- ◆ Picasso
- ◆ Monet
- ◆ Renoir
- ◆ Manet
- ◆ Cassat
- ◆ Van Gogh
- ◆ Warhol
- ◆ Gauguin
- ◆ Rodin
- ◆ Botticelli
- ◆ Rubens

16. Famous Scientists:

- • Thomas Edison
- • Sir Isaac Newton
- • Albert Einstein
- • Louis Pasteur
- • Marie Curie

17. Parts of the Body that are Essential to Life:

- ◆ Brain
- ◆ Heart

18. Person - Event:

- • (A) Civil Rights Leader - Martin Luther King
- • (B) Broke color barrier in major league baseball - Jackie Robinson
- • (C) Supreme Court Justice - Sandra Day O'Connor
- • (D) Villain during the war between the U.S. and Germany - Adolf Hitler
- • (E) Credited with discovering America - Christopher Columbus
- • (F) "Give me liberty or give me death" - Patrick Henry
- • (G) Wrote "The Declaration of Independence" - Thomas Jefferson

19. Colors of the Rainbow:

- ◆ Red
- ◆ Orange
- ◆ Yellow
- ◆ Green
- ◆ Blue
- ◆ Indigo
- ◆ Violet

20. Book Sources for Information:

- • Dictionary
- • Encyclopedia
- • Atlas
- • Almanac

21. American Rivers:

- ◆ Mississippi,
- ◆ Missouri
- ◆ Ohio
- ◆ Delaware
- ◆ Columbia
- ◆ Etc.

22. Plays by Shakespeare:

- "Romeo and Juliet"
- "Othello"
- "Twelfth Night"
- "Two Gentlemen of Verona"
- "The Tempest"
- "Hamlet"
- "Macbeth"
- "A Midsummer Night's Dream"
- "Richard II"
- "As You Like It"
- "Richard I"
- "Antony and Cleopatra"
- "King Lear"
- "Merchant of Venice"
- "Titus Andronicus"
- "Much Ado About Nothing"
- "Henry VI (parts 1, 2, & 3)"
- "Richard III"
- "Comedy of Error"
- "Taming of the Shrew"
- "Love's Labour's Lost"
- "King John"
- "Henry IV (parts 1 & 2)"
- "Henry V"
- "Julius Caesar"
- "The Merry Wives of Windsor"
- "Troilus and Cressida"
- "All's Well That Ends Well"
- "Measure for Measure"
- "Coriolanus"
- "Timon of Athens"
- "Pericles"
- "Cymbeline"
- "The Winter's Tale"
- "Henry VII"

23. Fractions to Decimals:

- 1/2 = .5
- 2/8 = .25
- 5/5 = 1.0
- 3/10 = .30

24. Story About Someone's Life:

- Biography
- Autobiography

25. States of Water:

- Gas (Water Vapor)
- Liquid (Water)
- Solid (Ice)

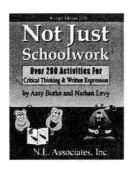

Dynamic Speakers
Creative Workshops
Relevant Topics

Nathan Levy, author of the <u>Stories with Holes</u> series and <u>There Are Those</u>, and other nationally known authors and speakers, can help your school or organization achieve positive results with children. We can work with you to provide a complete in-service package or have one of our presenters lead one of several informative and entertaining workshops.

Workshop Topics Include:

- Practical Activities for Teaching Gifted Children
Critical Thinking Skills

- Differentiating in the Regular Classroom

- How to Read, Write and Think Better

- Using <u>Stories with Holes</u> and Other Thinking Activities

- Powerful Strategies to Enhance the Learning of Your Gifted and Highly Capable Students

- Powerful Strategies to Help Your Students With Special Needs be More Successful Learners

- The Principal as an Educational Leader

and many more…

Nathan Levy, author and consultant

Nathan Levy is the author of more than 40 books which have sold almost 250,000 copies to teachers and parents in the US, Europe, Asia, South America, Australia and Africa. His unique <u>Stories with Holes</u> series continues to be proclaimed the most popular activity used in gifted, special education and regular classrooms by hundreds of educators. An extremely popular, dynamic speaker on thinking, writing and differentiation, Nathan is in high demand as a workshop leader in school and business settings. As a former school principal, company president, parent of four daughters and management trainer, Nathan's ability to transfer knowledge and strategies to audiences through humorous, thought provoking stories assures that participants leave with a plethora of new ways to approach their future endeavors.

Please write or call to receive workshop information.

NL Associates, Inc., P.O. Box 1199, Hightstown, NJ 08520-0399
(732) 656 - 7822
www.storieswithholes.com